MIEL   MILLECAMPS   TEFENKGI   V   YOU

JUMP START

ALEX

WALES

TO LET

How could I forget?
My worst nightmare!

25 YEARS EARLIER

Oh no!

Help!

Aaaah!

What are you doing? Put me down!

You've had a lucky escape there my boy! But a swarm of angry bees is nothing compared to what you'll get from your grandmother when she hears about this!

If only old George knew! I didn't have the heart to punish you after a shock like that!

Yes, I can honestly say I learned my lesson!

He's a bit rough, but he's got a good heart...

And it's funny, he really took me under his wing after that. He taught me all about beekeeping, all his tricks and secrets.

I think having only bees for company got on his nerves in the end.

I'll go and pay him a visit.

Good idea! He'll be really pleased to see you!

9

Oh it's you, my boy! When I saw that lorry I thought it might be the landlord coming to kick me out already...

So how are you George?

Come in and have a drink with me. You've got to try my mead, this year's is out of this world!

You're right, it's lovely!

Come on, let's go and see the bees!

Granny told me a bit about what's going on... When are you leaving? And what's going to happen to the hives?

The landlord's given me three months.

That's awful, and with honey of this quality! So all this is just going to disappear?

Unless...

Unless what?

Unless you took over my little cottage industry. You and the bees go back a long way... and I've taught you everything I know.

But where am I going to get the money? I've not got a penny. All I've got are loans, which I'm still having trouble paying off!

We could work something out...

But how? And what about you? If you're going to stay, you'll need money to pay the extra rent after the renovation.

We'll have to think about it...

It's unbelievable! He suggested I take over his business...

But I'm broke!

What a good idea! You should go and see a bank manager...

CARDIFF

It's all very vague.
No business plan... no security...
and I don't have the authority...
I'll send your file to head office...
But to be honest, I already know
what they're going to say.

No luck
so far!

BLUE
CREDIT

With the outstanding loans you've
already got, we can't help you.
But why don't you go to a bank that specialises
in microfinance for business start-ups?
There's one in town... here's the address.

You've come to the right place. But there are a few things you'll need to do first: draw up a plan, make your case, work out the figures and the forecasts. You can get help with all that.

We work closely with an organisation that's funded by the EU. Their mission is to help people who want to start a business but, for various reasons, can't get the traditional banks to listen to or support them.

So here's what I suggest you do…

Goodness me, you scare me when you act all serious like that!

How many pots of honey did you produce last year?

Er… three or four hundred… maybe more.

And how do you sell them? And for how much?

It varies… but I give lots of them away in the village, to family…

And what about the mead?

That's my own personal supply… It's sacrosanct!

OK George, we've got to be specific! If you want me to take over your business, I'll need the figures to persuade the organisation that's going to lend me the money…

NINE MONTHS LATER

You see, I was right to think big! We've produced almost twice as much honey!

And it pains me to say it, but your mead is almost better than mine!

Cheers!

Right, there's still more to do here, but I've got deliveries to make!

If I'd known all of this before, I would've thought twice about sneaking through that hedge.

Yes indeed, too late now! Curiosity's a bad character trait. Your grandmother should've kept a closer eye on you, ha ha ha!

NATALINE

MiLLE
CAMPS

At last! I couldn't have gone on any longer! A day like that really gives you an appetite!

Aren't you having anything to eat Nataline?

No, I don't know what's wrong with me... I've not been feeling too good lately.

I'm exhausted after that shoot. I'm going back to the hotel.

You're joking!? No way! It's party time tonight... Don't be such a diva...!

What do you want to drink? Mojitos all round? I'm paying!

Cheers, Nataline!

THE NEXT MORNING

Riga Airport, Latvia

Are you OK Nataline? You don't look as good as you do on the poster...

Yeah... OK girls, that's enough! You're wearing me out! You were the ones who made me go out last night!

In fact I...

Nataline? Nataline?

21

THREE DAYS LATER

Hello!

Hi, I know you! The would-be chocolate machine smasher!

Miss Lengel?

I understand that all this is a bit sudden for you. But we're here to help you build your future.

Yes, I do feel a bit lost...

What qualifications have you got?

I was studying history of art, but I gave it up to become a model.

When you were a child, were there any jobs you dreamed of doing?

Well, certainly not modelling...

No, I was more interested in business. My parents were self-employed. I've always fancied running my own business... But it's a bit late now. I know nothing about management.

It's never too late! We offer management courses, with funding from Europe, and they're a solid foundation for branching out on your own. All you need is motivation and time.

Well, I've got time now. And a bit of money put aside. My career did pay well.

Perfect! We'll take care of the training. And it's up to you to come up with a plan and think it through.

We must stop meeting like this!

Sit down, let me buy you a drink.

I'm Nataline.

I'm Julia. So you talked to them too? What are you planning on doing?

I don't know yet, but I'm giving up modelling. I need a healthier life. I'm going to sign up for this management course. I've got nothing to lose.

Not really my thing, management... but I'm turning over a new leaf too... No more nightlife for me, I want to get back to the things I used to love doing. I've always adored cooking.

Talking of food, I really fancy a salad. Where shall we go?

The restaurants round here aren't great...

That's what you call a tomato! What an amazing taste!

And you can guarantee we'll get two crates of assorted fruit and vegetables a day?

Yes, my nephew will deliver them to you.

Excellent! It's a deal. See you soon!

Things are looking pretty good eh?

I can't wait to get started!

Now let's head for the town centre. We're going to the Organic and Regional Produce Fair. There's a honey producer from Wales I'd like to meet.

A FEW DAYS LATER

Wait, Julia! This moment needs to be immortalised on film!

Your turn!

Brilliant Nataline! Looks like you've been doing it all your life!

Looks like we've got off to a good start!

Just you wait! This is only the first step... We could launch our own brand of organic produce and open a greengrocer's... And I've still got a few more ideas up my sleeve...!

IVANA

SIHANOUKVILLE, CAMBODIA

Will you take a dozen langoustines, Ivana? I'll give you a good price!

They look wonderful, Chhim! Can I trade you something I made, for half a dozen?

OK, I'll sell it to a tourist.

You've got more of a head for business than me.

Ivana…

Phone call for you from Italy.

Yes, speaking...

My name's Ferreri. I'm a notary. I've had real trouble finding you. It's about your father.

I'm very sorry to have to tell you that he passed away.

... when?

Three weeks ago. You're needed back in Milan to deal with his estate.

I can't even afford a beer, let alone a ticket to Milan...

We'll have a whip round, Ivana.

That's so sweet of you girls. I'll pay you back with interest on top when everything's settled.

Any spare change Your Highness, for something to eat?

Here, it's not much, but I'm almost broke.

I'd like a room for one night please.

I'm going to have to ask you to pay in advance.

Pfff, I'm in the deep end now.

36

What's my bag doing there?

You only booked in for one night didn't you?

Rooms have to be vacated by 11 a.m. Those are the rules.

Come under here where it's dry, Your Majesty.

Thanks, I've just been thrown out of my hotel and I don't know where I'm going to spend the night... I've not got a penny left.

Don't panic, you can stay in our royal suite. Fancy a drink to raise your spirits?

The rain's stopped now, so we can go back to our apartments.

Come with us, it's only 10 minutes away.

It's a bit basic, but at least no one bothers us here...

So far, anyway.

Brrrrr! It's not very warm. But you've made it nice in here.

What are all these crates of fabric doing here?

Oh them, they're scraps from the factory next door.

They throw them away every day in containers and we thought we could use them.

Your friends are going to eat well again I see!

I know. It's against the rules, but I can't help myself, I just love them!

That's a work of art. You're really gifted! I wouldn't mind one of those myself!

Wow! You've got magic hands!

I want to make you all one. But I'll need a hand!

42

So that's the whole story…

I really think you should come to the Piccolo Mondo centre.

We got support from the European Social Fund to open a shop selling second-hand clothing.

And our project was designed, among other reasons, to help talented people like you.

And now... Surprise!

Happy birthday Sergio!

This is the best 50th birthday party I've ever had!

A toast: to life!

DIMITRA

SIBIU, ROMANIA

There you go, all done. You can go back out to play now, Raluca. But be careful, OK? The wound hasn't completely healed yet.

Don't you feel well?

If you want to help me, go and hang out the washing.

A little kiss to help my favourite daddy along!

Try these strawberries, Malva darling!

Ouch!

Tee hee!

You're going to pay for that, Raluca… You little scumbag!

You'll have to catch me first! Ha ha!

Ouch! Let me go! You're hurting me!

That's enough now children! Don't you think there's enough violence in the world already? Raluca, aren't you ashamed of yourself?

She started it!

Liar!

Malva, get back indoors! And you, keep your nose out of other people's business!

Hello. I'm Nora, from the health and welfare centre. Don't hesitate to drop in and see us if you need anything at all.

What a cheek! She probably thinks I'm not capable of bringing up my own children! And you, Malva, I'm not finished with you yet!

51

What are you doing here? You look bored…

I'm not, but it's no fun at home. When my mother gets angry, I prefer to stay out of the way.

She's quite a character, your mum. She doesn't seem very easy-going…

It's because of the baby she's expecting. She's in pain, so she gets all worked up.

She really must come and see us at the centre!

No chance! Unless she decides to herself, she won't come.

We'll have to find a solution then.

What about you? Tell me a bit about yourself.

Are you OK mum?

Yes, yes… I just need to rest… Ow! My God!

Why don't you go and see a doctor!?

Leave me alone. Go and play outside.

THE NEXT DAY

Oh hello Malva. How nice to see you.

Did you bring your drawings?

Yes! Lots of them!

Come on then, let's see them.

Look Nora, that's me, the captain!

You look very pretty and so does your uniform! And I really like the cabin in the shape of a house.

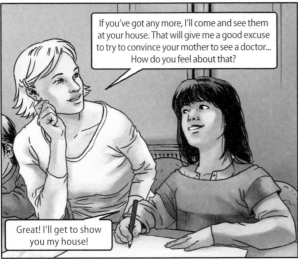

If you've got any more, I'll come and see them at your house. That will give me a good excuse to try to convince your mother to see a doctor... How do you feel about that?

Great! I'll get to show you my house!

Oh please don't stop playing! It's wonderful. Is that a piece by Grigoras Dinicu?

Yes, do you know it!?

Ow!

Help! Mum! I've cut myself! It's bleeding really badly!!!

Come here!

Lucky I always keep my first aid kit with me... all part of the job.

Thank you, thank you! For looking after him and Malva...

What about you? How's your pregnancy going?

Hmm, not so good. It's not like my other pregnancies... I often get terrible pains and I have to lie down.

Promise me you'll drop by the centre tomorrow. I'll tell the doctor about you... You'll see, he's very nice and good at his job.

I'm not asking for charity... I don't have any money.

Don't worry, Dimitra. We're financed by the European Social Fund. Healthcare's free.

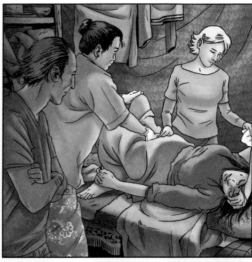

Additional information

Alex, Nataline, Ivana and Dimitra successfully changed the course of their lives thanks to the programmes financed by the European Social Fund (ESF).

But what exactly is the ESF?

The ESF was created more than 50 years ago, in 1957, to be precise. It is the main financial instrument used by the European Union for investing in people. Its goal is to promote employment by improving workers' prospects. It provides support, for example, to individuals who have particular difficulties in finding a job, including women, young people and elderly workers. It also provides support to businesses and young entrepreneurs. The Fund also invests in lifelong education and training.

The ESF does not work alone; it is at the core of a partnership comprising multiple players. The projects that it supports are co-funded by the Member States and put forward by educational and training institutions, associations, trade unions, etc. These projects are selected by the national authorities to meet the requirements of specific countries and regions.

Today, the ESF is a real success story. Each year, the ESF invests EUR 10 billion in the financing of various projects across the 27 Member States. This investment is used to improve the lives of 10 million individuals each year, by helping them to find a job or to advance in their careers.

From reality to fiction

The comic book *Jump start* is based on four true events. The European Commission gathered personal accounts from 54 EU citizens, all of whom had benefited from ESF-funded programmes. In front of the camera, they speak about their own experiences and of the path that led them to new employment and training opportunities. To see these personal accounts, visit: http://ec.europa.eu/employment_social/esf/video/videos_en.htm

The authors

Text

Rudi Miel

Born in Tournai, in 1965, Rudi Miel has a degree in journalism. Communications consultant and comic book scriptwriter, he is the co-author of *Les eaux blessées* (*Troubled waters*), published by the European Parliament, which won the award for best use of comic books in advertising at Angoulême in 2003. He wrote the text for *L'arbre des deux printemps* (*Tree of the two springs*) (illustrated by Will & Co — published by Le Lombard), which won the award for best foreign comic book at Sobreda (Portugal) in 2001. Along with C. Cuadra and P. Teng, Rudi Miel is also co-author of *L'ordre impair* (*Odd order*) (Le Lombard), which was published in full at the end of 2009. When writing *Jump start*, he worked in collaboration with scriptwriter Jean-Luc Cornette.

Illustrations

Maud Millecamps — Nataline

Born in Charleroi in 1982, Maud Millecamps attended the École Supérieure des Arts Saint-Luc, in Liège, and the Académie des Beaux-Arts, in Brussels. She was part of the collective that produced *Amour & désir* (*Love and desire*) for the publishing house La boîte à bulles in 2008, before bringing out her first cartoon album, *Les gens urbains* (*Urbanites*), scripted by Jean-Luc Cornette and published by Quadrants in 2010. Maud lives in Brussels.

Alexandre Tefenkgi — Alex

Born in 1979, Alexandre Tefenkgi is originally from Montpellier. After studying at the École Supérieure des Arts Saint-Luc, in Liège, he met comic book artist Mauricet, with whom he now works and shares a studio. He produced a few short stories for *Spirou* magazine before bringing out his first cartoon album *Tranquille courage* (*Quiet courage*), published by Bamboo.

Vanyda — Ivana

Of French and Laotian descent, Vanyda was born in 1979. It was during her studies at l'Académie des Beaux-Arts (the Academy of Fine Arts) at Tournai, where she specialised in comic books, that she met François Duprat, who drew the scenes for Ivana (colours by Virginie Vidal), and with whom she worked on the comic book *L'année du dragon* (*Year of the dragon*) (published by Carabas). In her comic books, she evokes an intimate and contemporary universe, similar to the one depicted in *L'immeuble d'en face* (*The building opposite*) (Boite à Bulles), where we follow the day-to-day lives of neighbours living on the same floor, or in the comic book *Celle que ...* (*The one ...*) (Dargaud), which recounts the story of a young girl growing up and making the transition to secondary school.

You — Dimitra

Born in South Korea in 1978, You is a self-taught comic book artist. After studying computer graphics, she illustrated several children's books, including three in the *Moi je sais* (*I know*) collection, published by Auzou. Her first cartoon album appeared in the *Sorcières* (*Witches*) series, published by Dupuis. She is currently working for the same publisher on a new story set in the late 19th century.